SFX FOR ALL HOME KEYBOARDS

Exclusive distributors:
Music Sales Limited
8/9 Frith Street,
London W1V 5TZ, England.

Music Sales Pty Limited
120 Rothschild Avenue,
Rosebery, NSW 2018, Australia.

This book © Copyright 1989 by Wise Publications

UK ISBN 0.7119.1801.5
Order No. AM74394

Art direction by Mike Bell
Compiled by Peter Evans
Arranged by Peter Lavender
Music processed by Barnes Music Engraving
Typeset by Capital Setters

Music Sales' complete catalogue lists thousands of
titles and is free from your local music shop,
or direct from Music Sales Limited.
Please send £1 in stamps for postage to
Music Sales Limited, 8/9 Frith Street, London W1V 5TZ.

Printed in the United Kingdom by
Loader Jackson Printers Limited, Arlesey, Bedfordshire.

Wise Publications
London/New York/Sydney/Cologne

The ABC of SFX Music

In SFX music, the melody is clearly written in large lettered notes. Each note can easily be located on your keyboard and then played with the right hand.

The songs in SFX music books are all written in the following keyboard range. The symbol at the beginning of the music staff is the treble clef, indicating the notes are played with the right hand:

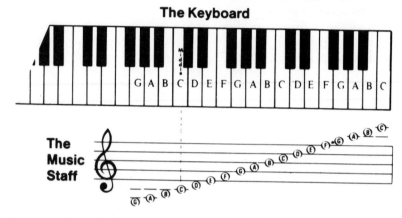

The Sharp Sign (♯) will sometimes appear before a music note. Simply play the *black key* to the *right* of the *white key:*

The Flat Sign (♭) placed before a note tells you to play the *black key* that lies to the *left* of the *white key:*

The Music Staff is divided into equal sections by vertical lines called *Bar Lines*. Each section is a *Measure*. The end of a piece of music is marked by a double bar line.

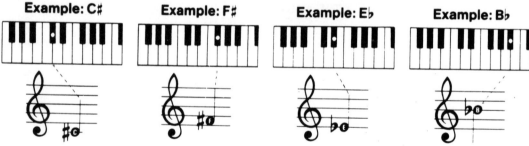

All music is played in time to a *beat*. The six types of notes most often used in SFX music all have a *time value* that relates to the beat:

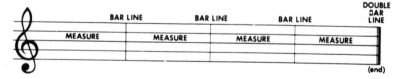

Whole note	Dotted half note	Half note	Dotted quarter note	Quarter note	Eighth note
4 Beats	3 Beats	2 Beats	1½ Beats	1 Beat	½ Beat

The Rest is a silent break in the music. The symbols are written in the staff, and like music notes, rests each have a time value:

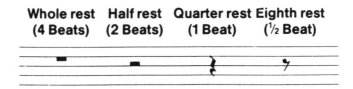

Whole rest (4 Beats)	Half rest (2 Beats)	Quarter rest (1 Beat)	Eighth rest (½ Beat)

The Time Signature comprises two numbers at the beginning of the music, after the treble clef sign. The top number shows the amount of beats in each measure. The bottom number indicates the type of note that will receive *one* beat. These are the most popular time signatures. The lower number 4 represents the quarter note:

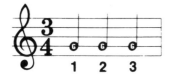

The Tie is a curved line that connects two consecutive notes on the same line or in the same space in the staff. When a tie appears in the music, play the first note and sustain the sound for the *total* time value of the two notes:

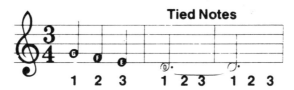

Tied Notes

Repeat Signs are two dots alongside double bar lines. They indicate that all the music in between the pairs of repeat signs is to be played through again:

Quite often there will only be one repeat sign at the end of a passage of music. The repeat is then made from the very beginning:

Double Endings are sections of music with staff repeat signs. 1st and 2nd time brackets above the staff indicate where a short 'skip' is to be made in the music after the repeat has been played:

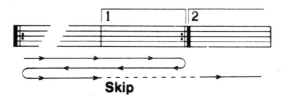

Skip

Left Hand Keyboard Accompaniment. SFX music has Major and Minor chords clearly written above the staff. The optional 'seventh' type of chord is shown with the 7 outside the chord frame:

Your keyboard Owner's Manual will explain how these chords are played with your left hand.

Conventional (Fingered) Chords can also be used. **The SFX Master Chord Chart** in this book shows the most practical chord positions for this type of left hand accompaniment.

Devoted To You

Suggested Registration: ACOUSTIC GUITAR OR HARMONICA
Rhythm: COUNTRY ROCK
Tempo: MEDIUM

Words & Music by
Boudleaux Bryant

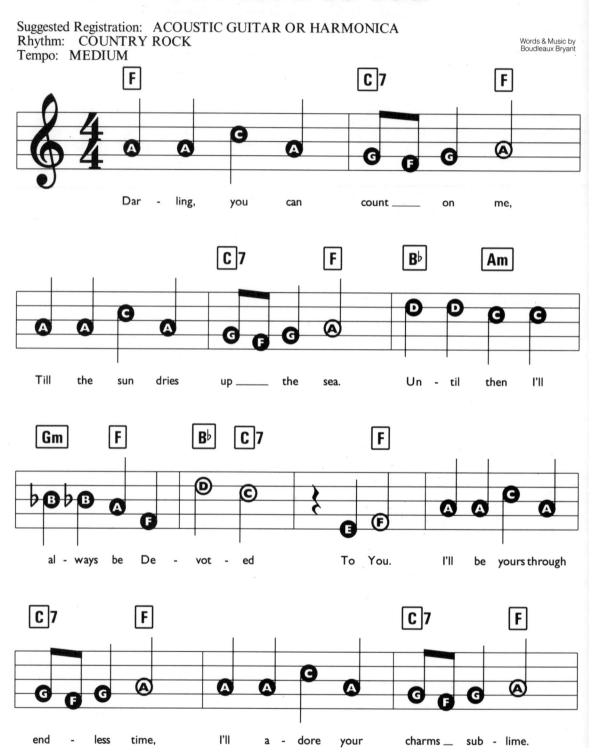

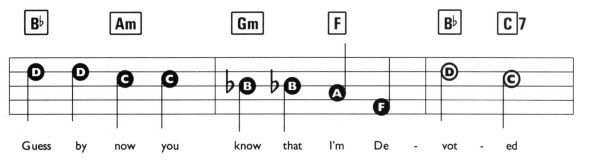

Guess by now you know that I'm De - vot - ed

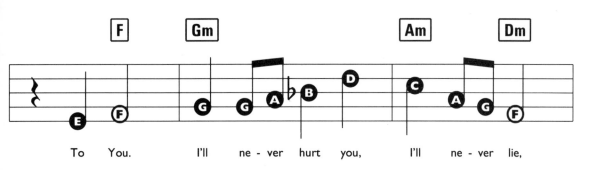

To You. I'll ne - ver hurt you, I'll ne - ver lie,

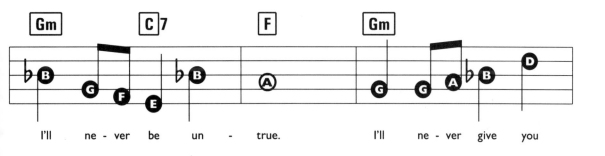

I'll ne - ver be un - true. I'll ne - ver give you

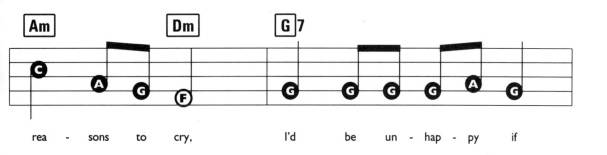

rea - sons to cry, I'd be un - hap - py if

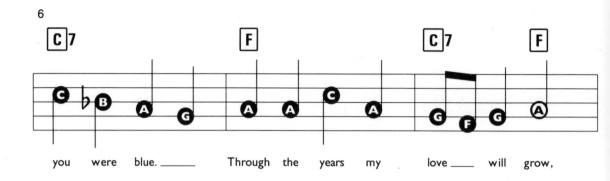

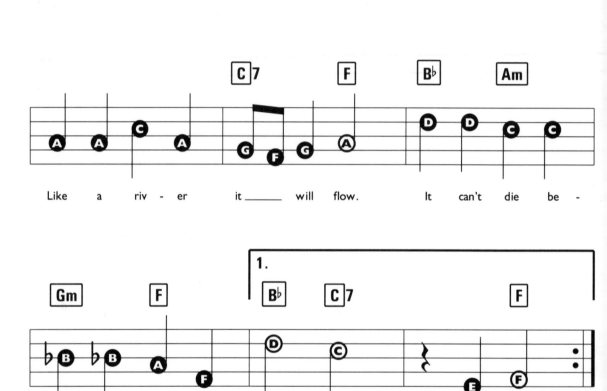

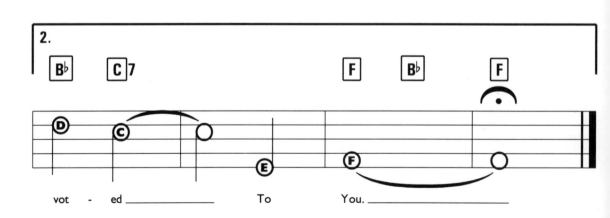

Evergreen

Suggested Registration: FLUTE OR STRINGS
Rhythm: BALLAD
Tempo: MEDIUM

Words by Paul Williams
Music by Barbra Streisand

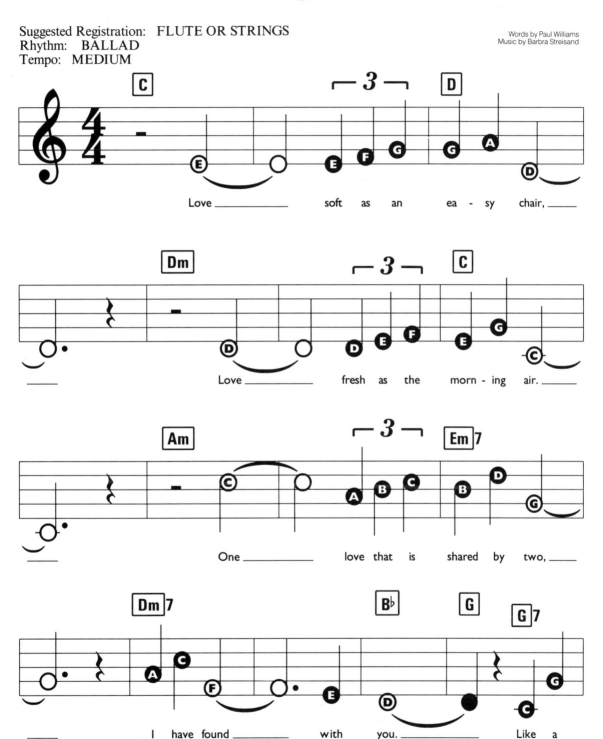

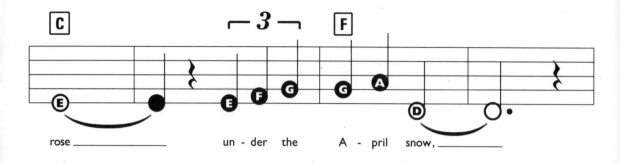

rose _____ un - der the A - pril snow, _____

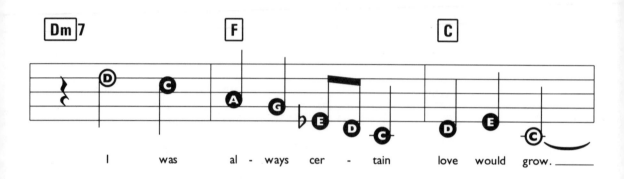

I was al - ways cer - tain love would grow. _____

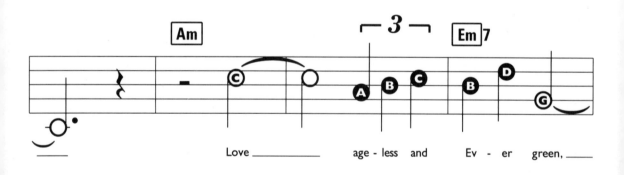

_____ Love _____ age - less and Ev - er green, _____

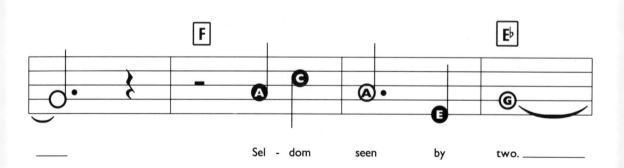

_____ Sel - dom seen by two. _____

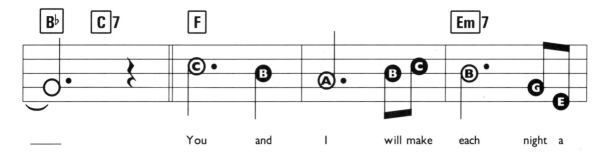

You and I will make each night a

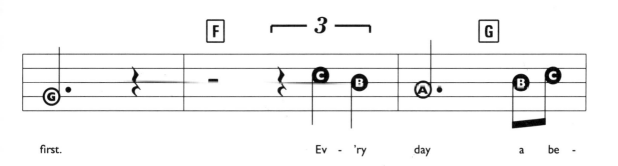

first.   Ev - 'ry   day   a   be -

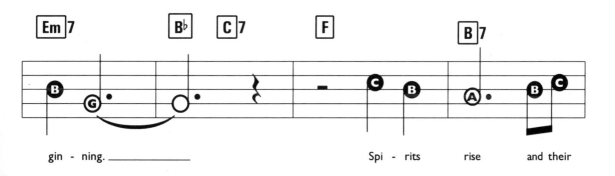

gin - ning. _____   Spi - rits   rise   and their

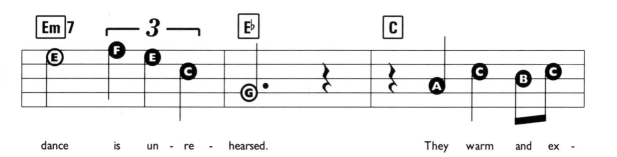

dance   is   un - re - hearsed.   They   warm   and ex -

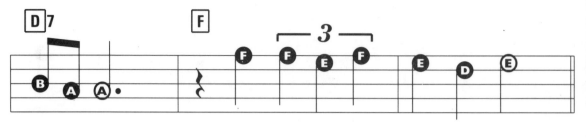

cite _____ us,   'Cause   we   have   the   bright   -   est

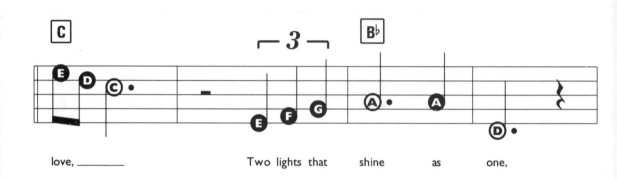

love, _____   Two lights that   shine   as   one,

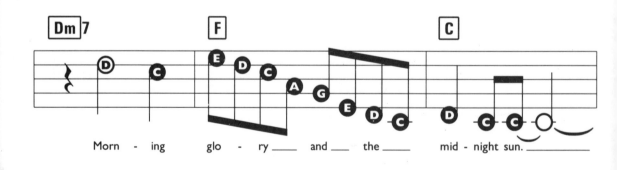

Morn - ing   glo - ry ___ and ___ the ___ mid - night sun. _____

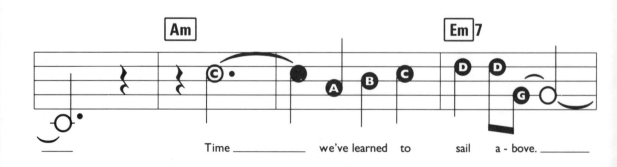

_____   Time _____ we've learned to   sail   a - bove. _____

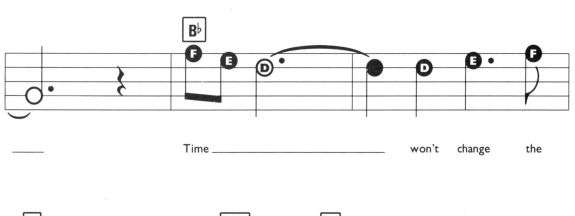

Time _____ won't change the

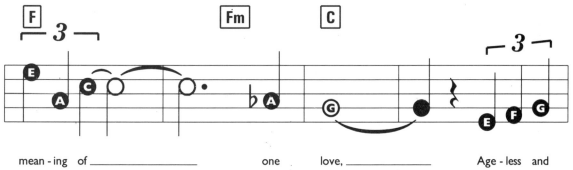

mean - ing of _____ one love, _____ Age - less and

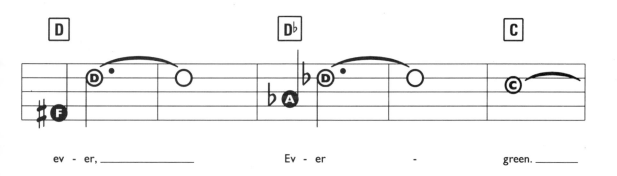

ev - er, _____ Ev - er - green. _____

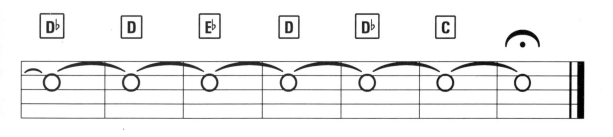

Just The Two Of Us

Suggested Registration: JAZZ ORGAN OR ACOUSTIC GUITAR
Rhythm: LATIN ROCK OR BOSSANOVA
Tempo: MEDIUM

Words & Music by Ralph MacDonald,
William Salter & Bill Withers

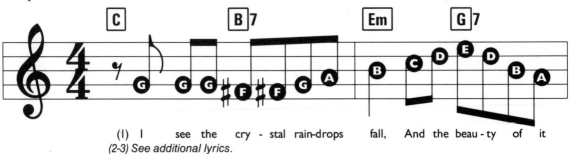

(1) I see the cry - stal rain-drops fall, And the beau - ty of it
(2-3) See additional lyrics.

all is when the sun ___ comes shin - ing through. ___

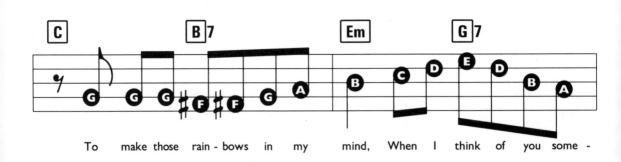

To make those rain - bows in my mind, When I think of you some -

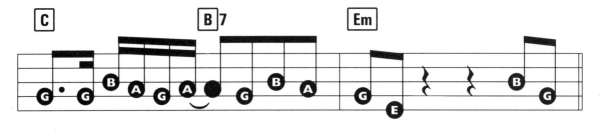

time, And I want to spend __ some - time with you. _____ Just The

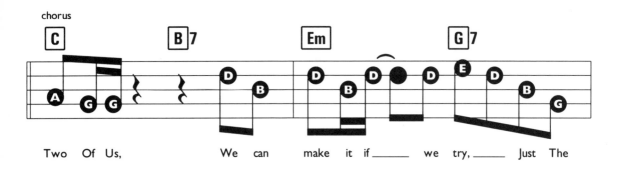

chorus

Two Of Us, We can make it if _____ we try, _____ Just The

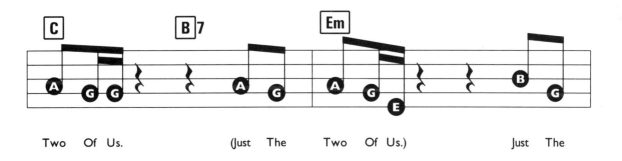

Two Of Us. (Just The Two Of Us.) Just The

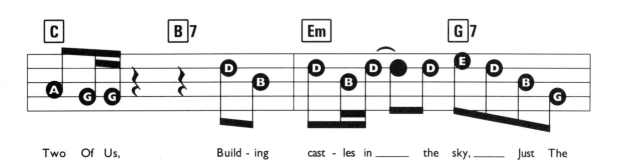

Two Of Us, Build - ing cast - les in _____ the sky, _____ Just The

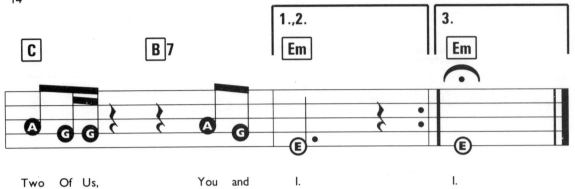

Two Of Us, You and I. I.

Verse 2:
We look for love, no time for tears,
Wasted water all that is,
And it don't make no flowers grow.
Good things might come to those who wait,
Not for those who wait too late,
We gotta go for all we know.
(Chorus)

Verse 3:
I hear the crystal raindrops fall,
On the window down the hall,
And it becomes the morning dew.
And darlin' when the morning comes,
And I see the morning sun,
I want to be the one with you.
(Chorus)

Missing You

Suggested Registration: PIANO OR VIBRAPHONE
Rhythm: ROCK (8 BEAT)
Tempo: MEDIUM

Words & Music by
Chris De Burgh

16

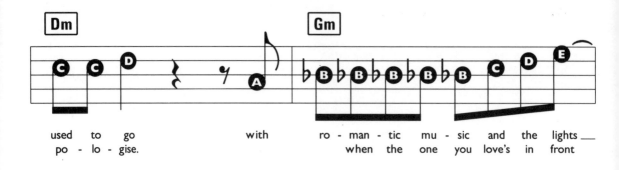

used to go — with — ro - man - tic mu - sic and the lights___
po - lo - gise. — when the one you love's in front

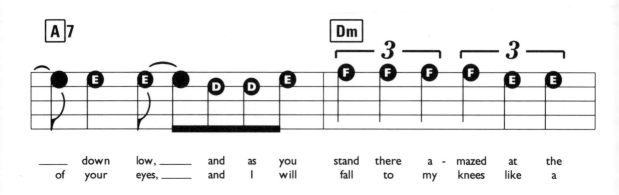

___ down low, ___ and as you stand there a - mazed at the
of your eyes, ___ and I will fall to my knees like a

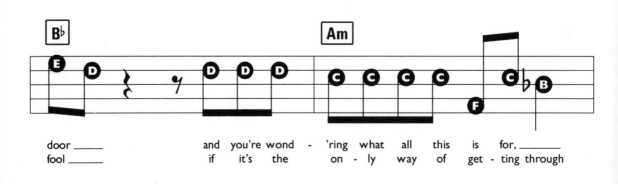

door ___ and you're wond - 'ring what all this is for, ___
fool ___ if it's the on - ly way of get - ting through

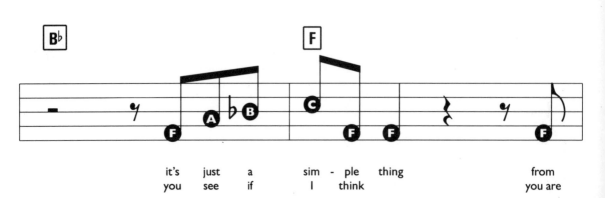

it's just a sim - ple thing from
you see if I think you are

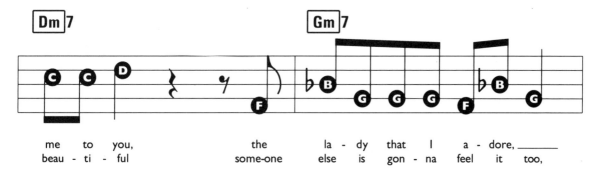

	Dm7				Gm7			
me	to you,			the	la - dy	that I	a - dore,_____	
beau -	ti - ful			some-one	else is	gon - na	feel it	too,

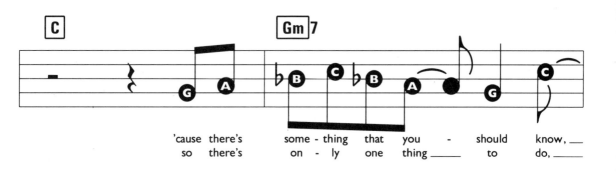

C ... Gm7

| 'cause | there's | some - thing | that | you - | should | know, _ |
| so | there's | on - ly | one | thing ____ | to | do, ____ |

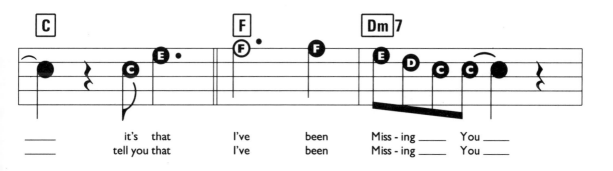

C ... F ... Dm7

| _____ | it's that | I've | been | Miss - ing ____ You ____ |
| _____ | tell you that | I've | been | Miss - ing ____ You ____ |

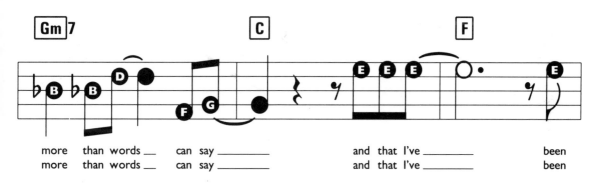

Gm7 ... C ... F

| more | than words _ | can say ____ | and that I've _____ | been |
| more | than words _ | can say ____ | and that I've _____ | been |

18

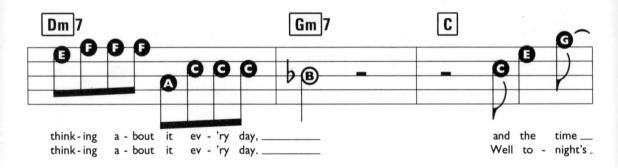

think-ing a - bout it ev - 'ry day, _____ and the time __
think-ing a - bout it ev - 'ry day. _____ Well to - night's __

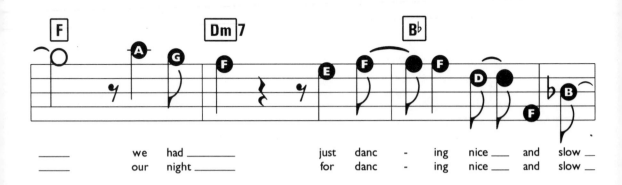

_____ we had _____ just danc - ing nice __ and slow __
_____ our night _____ for danc - ing nice __ and slow __

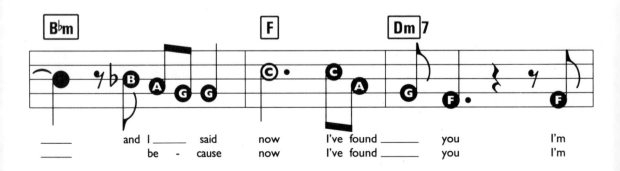

_____ and I _____ said now I've found _____ you I'm
_____ be - cause now I've found _____ you I'm

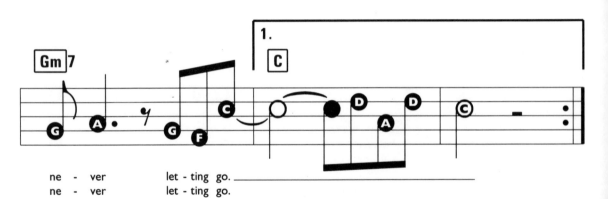

ne - ver let - ting go. _____
ne - ver let - ting go.

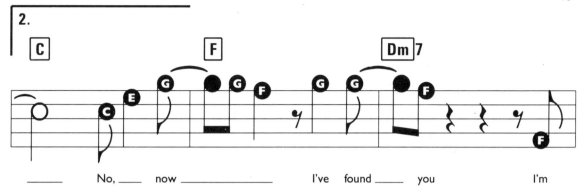

No, ____ now _____ I've found ____ you I'm

ne - ver let - ting go. _____

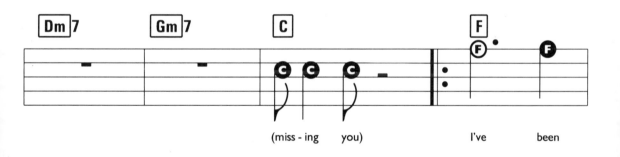

(miss - ing you) I've been

Repeat to fade

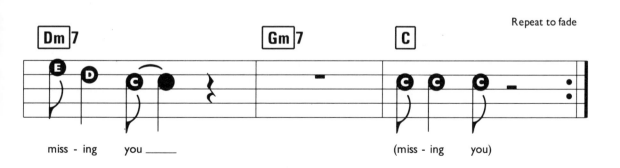

miss - ing you ____ (miss - ing you)

Loving Her Was Easier
(Than Anything I'll Ever Do Again)

Suggested Registration: ACOUSTIC GUITAR OR PIANO
Rhythm: COUNTRY ROCK
Tempo: MEDIUM

Words & Music by
Kris Kristofferson

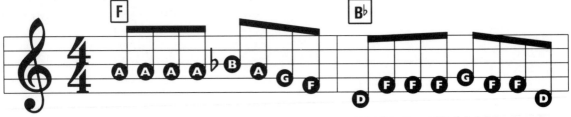

I have seen the morn-ing burn-ing gol-den on the moun-tain in the
Wak-ing in the morn-ing to the feel-ing of her fin-gers on my

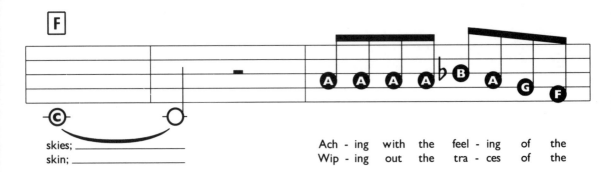

skies; _____
skin; _____

Ach-ing with the feel-ing of the
Wip-ing out the tra-ces of the

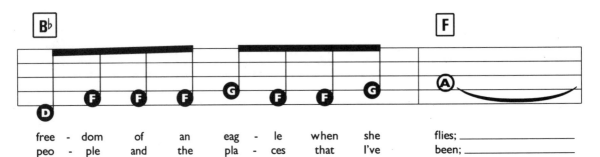

free - dom of an eag - le when she flies; _____
peo - ple and the pla - ces that I've been; _____

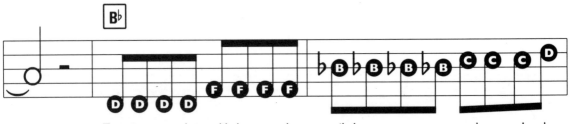

_____ Turn-ing on the world, the way she smiled up - on my soul as I lay
_____ Teach-ing me that yes-ter-day was some-thing that I ne-ver thought of

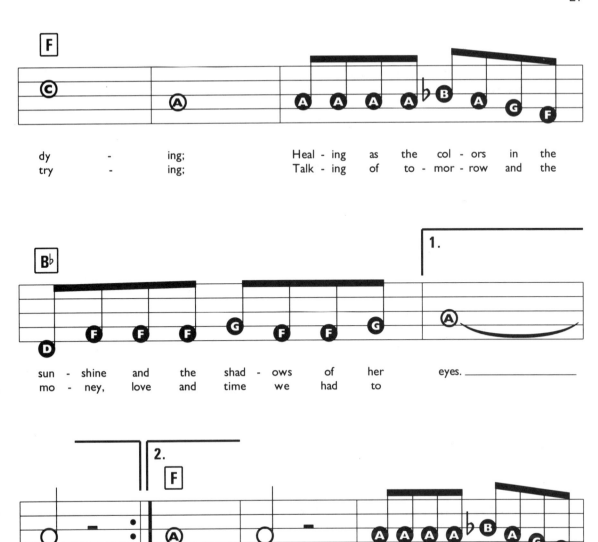

F

© C   Ⓐ   Ⓐ Ⓐ Ⓐ Ⓐ♭Ⓑ Ⓐ Ⓖ Ⓕ

dy - ing;   Heal - ing   as   the   col - ors   in   the
try - ing;   Talk - ing   of   to - mor - row   and   the

B♭   1.

Ⓓ Ⓕ Ⓕ Ⓕ Ⓖ Ⓕ Ⓕ Ⓖ   Ⓐ

sun - shine   and   the   shad - ows   of   her   eyes. _____
mo - ney,   love   and   time   we   had   to

2. F

Ⓐ   Ⓐ Ⓐ Ⓐ Ⓐ♭Ⓑ Ⓐ Ⓖ Ⓕ

____   spend. _____   Lov - ing Her Was Eas - i - er Than

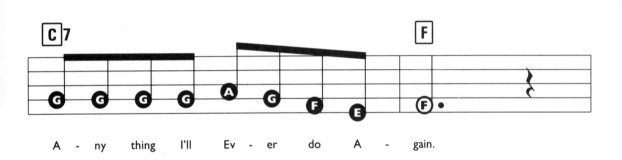

C 7   F

Ⓖ Ⓖ Ⓖ Ⓖ Ⓐ Ⓖ Ⓕ Ⓔ   Ⓕ•

A - ny   thing   I'll   Ev - er   do   A - gain.

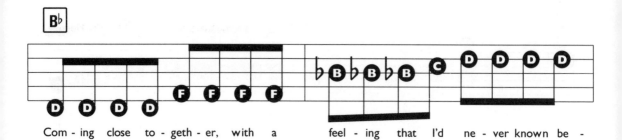

Com - ing close to - geth - er, with a feel - ing that I'd ne - ver known be -

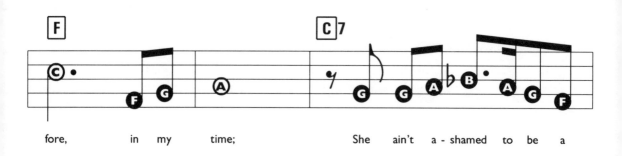

fore, in my time; She ain't a - shamed to be a

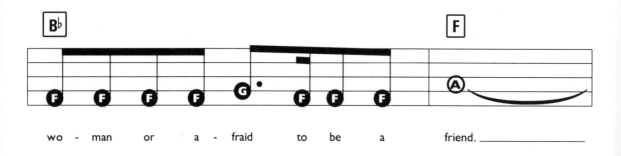

wo - man or a - fraid to be a friend. _____

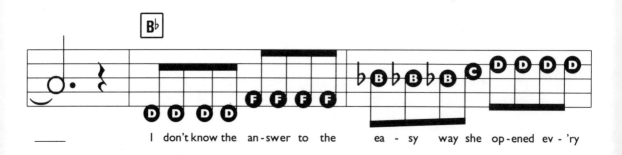

_____ I don't know the an - swer to the ea - sy way she op - ened ev - 'ry

23

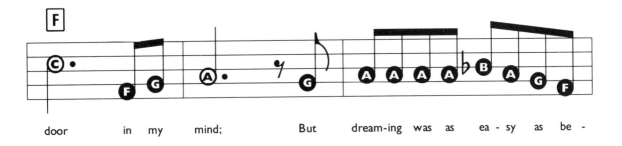

door in my mind; But dream-ing was as ea - sy as be -

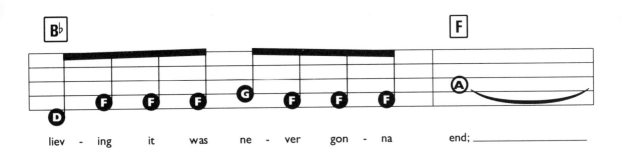

liev - ing it was ne - ver gon - na end;

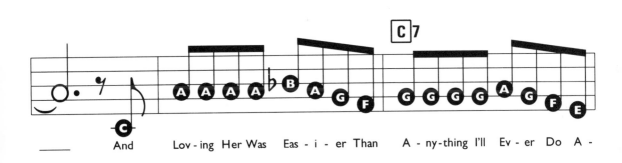

And Lov-ing Her Was Eas - i - er Than A - ny-thing I'll Ev - er Do A-

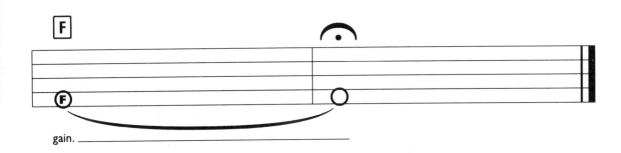

gain.

Portrait Of My Love

Suggested Registration: TRUMPET OR STRINGS.
Rhythm: BALLAD
Tempo: MEDIUM

Words by David West
Music by Cyril Ornadel

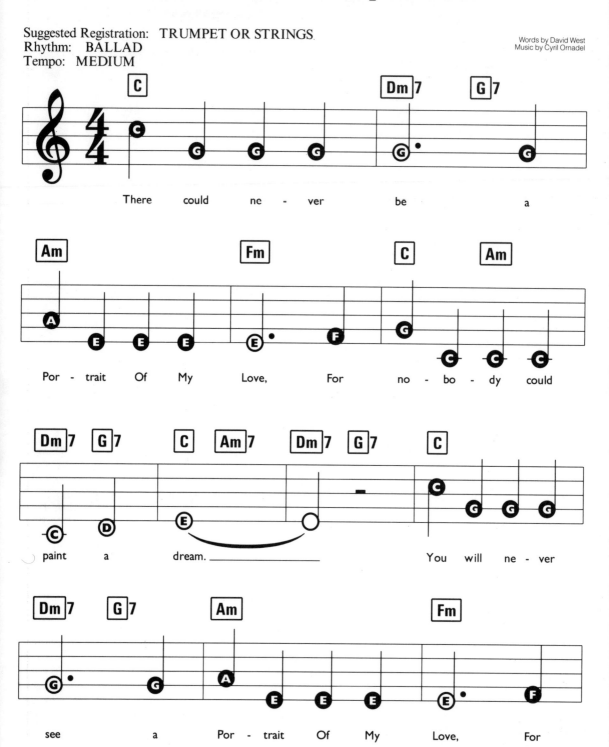

SFX
FOR ALL
PORTABLE KEYBOARDS

SFX music series goes on.
Designed for musicians or complete beginners.
The notation allows you to play popular music in minutes.
Famous popular songs in all editions.
Build your own SFX library with the complete Series.

SFX songbooks can also be used for piano, organ,
melody instruments, guitar, all electronic keyboards–
and vocal.

Start Playing Keyboard 1
by Peter Lavender
First book in an easy-to-follow course which starts you playing electronic keyboard right away. No knowledge of music needed. Teaches you 28 popular songs.

Start Playing Keyboard 2
by Peter Lavender
Play 'fingered' chords with your left hand, improve your sight reading and playing technique. Progress easily from SFX letter-note music to standard notation. 16 popular numbers including 'We've Only Just Begun', 'Yellow Submarine' and 'In The Hall Of The Mountain King'.

SFX – 1: Super Pops
Seventeen hits including: 'Love Me Tender', 'Annie's Song', 'Tie A Yellow Ribbon'.

SFX – 2: Rock Sounds
'Jailhouse Rock', '. . . Blue Suede Shoes', 'All Shook Up', and twelve more big hits.

SFX – 3: Beatles Hits
Nineteen famous Beatles hits including: 'Can't Buy Me Love', 'Yesterday', 'Hey Jude'.

SFX – 4: Latin Rhythms
Twenty famous hits including: 'The Girl From Ipanema', 'Quando, Quando, Quando', 'Brazil'.

SFX – 5: 70's and 80's Gold
Eighteen famous hits including: 'Imagine', 'Just The Way You Are', 'Sing'.

SFX – 6: Country Music
Twenty famous hits including: 'Don't It Make My Brown Eyes Blue', 'Cotton Jenny', 'Lucille'.

SFX – 7: The Police
Sixteen of their greatest hits including: 'Roxanne', 'Message In A Bottle', 'Every Breath You Take'.

SFX – 8: Duran Duran
Fifteen great hits including: 'Rio', 'Planet Earth', 'Union Of The Snake'.

SFX – 9: Easy Favourites
Twenty-two all-time hits including: 'After The Ball', 'Beer Barrel Polka', 'Little Brown Jug'.

THE SFX SE

SFX – 10: Classical Themes
Twenty famous themes including: 'Ave Maria', 'Can Can Polka', 'Hallelujah Chorus'.

SFX – 11: Musical Memories
Twenty hits including: 'Chanson D'Amour', 'Don't Cry For Me Argentina', 'Strangers In The Night'.

SFX – 12: Paul Simon
Sixteen hits including: 'Bridge Over Troubled Water', 'Cecilia', 'Mrs Robinson', 'The Boxer'.

SFX – 13: Michael Jackson
Thirteen hits including: 'Beat It', 'Ben', 'One Day In Your Life', 'Thriller'.

SFX – 14: Richard Clayderman
Fourteen hits including: 'Ballade Pour Adeline', 'L'Enfant et La Mer', 'My Way'.

SFX – 15: Stevie Wonder
Fifteen hits including: 'For Once In My Life', 'My Cherie Amour', 'You Are The Sunshine Of My Life'.

SFX – 16: Beatles No. 2
Twenty of their most famous numbers including: 'All My Loving' and 'Paperback Writer'.

SFX – 17: Film & TV Themes
Seventeen melodies from favourite shows. Includes: 'Edelweiss', 'Fiddler On The Roof'.

SFX – 18: Children's Songs
Sixteen of today's songs which are great favourites with children. Includes: 'Nellie The Elephant'.

SFX – 19: Christmas Songs
Nineteen songs and carols both traditional and modern. From 'Silent Night' to 'Mary's Boy Child'.

SFX – 20: Nursery Rhymes
'Baa Baa Black Sheep', 'Little Jack Horner' – more than 30 songs loved by children everywhere.

SFX – 21: Super Pops 2
Today's pops – 'EastEnders Theme', 'The Power Of Love' and 9 more favourites.

SFX – 22: Jazz & Blues
'Bugle Call Rag', 'Satin Doll', 'Take The 'A' Train' – 17 numbers popular with jazz fans.

IES GOES ON...

SFX – 23: Showtunes
Seventeen numbers from great shows such as 'Cabaret', 'Tell Me On A Sunday' and 'Chorus Line'.

SFX – 24: Walt Disney
'A Spoonful Of Sugar', 'Bibbidi-Bobbidi-Boo', 'The Bare Necessities' and 19 more Disney favourites.

SFX – 25: Phil Collins
'Sussudio', 'One More Night', 'Against All Odds' – 13 famous Phil Collins songs.

SFX – 26: Pub Singalong
Twenty-three famous pub songs including 'Lambeth Walk', 'Glorious Beer' and 'We'll Meet Again'.

SFX – 27: Hooked On Classics
Twenty-four popular classics including 'Eine Kleine Nachtmusik', 'Ode To Joy' and 'Land Of Hope And Glory'.

SFX – 28: Superpops 3
Eleven great chart hits including 'Born In The USA', 'Nothing's Gonna Stop Us Now' and 'What's Love Got To Do With It'.

SFX – 29: TV Themes
Sixteen favourite TV Themes including 'EastEnders', 'Moonlighting' and ' 'Allo 'Allo'.

ORDER FORM

Please write the quantities you require in the space against each book.
Terms: Strictly net monthly.

From _____

Address _____

Account number (if any) _____ Date _____

SFX Series

Beatles Hits	AM 33093	£3.50		Paul Simon	AM 37615	£3.50	
Beatles No.2	AM 39660	£3.50		Phil Collins	AM 64809	£3.50	
Children's Songs	AM 38811	£3.50		Police	AM 36807	£3.50	
Christmas Songs	AM 39686	£3.50		Pub Singalong	AM 66572	£3.50	
Classical Themes	AM 36831	£3.50		Richard Clayderman	AM 37995	£3.50	
Country Music	AM 33101	£3.50		Rock Sounds	AM 33127	£3.50	
Duran Duran	AM 36815	£3.50		70's and 80's Gold	AM 33135	£3.50	
Easy Favourites	AM 36823	£3.50		Showtunes	AM 63140	£3.50	
Film & TV Themes	AM 39678	£3.50		Start Playing Keyboard 1	AM 36906	£3.50	
Hooked On Classics	AM 66580	£3.50		Start Playing Keyboard 2	AM 65749	£3.50	
Jazz & Blues	AM 63132	£3.50		Stevie Wonder	AM 38019	£3.50	
Latin Rhythms	AM 33143	£3.50		Super Pops	AM 33119	£3.50	
Michael Jackson	AM 37987	£3.50		Super Pops 2	AM 63165	£3.50	
Musical Memories	AM 36849	£3.50		Super Pops 3	AM 66606	£3.50	
Nursery Rhymes	AM 63157	£3.50		TV Themes	AM 66598	£3.50	
				Walt Disney	AM 64817	£3.50	

Available Now from your local music shop, or in case of difficulty direct from:
Music Sales Limited, Newmarket Road, Bury St. Edmunds, Suffolk IP33 3YB.

25

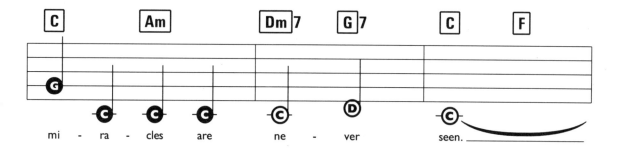

mi - ra - cles are ne - ver seen. _____

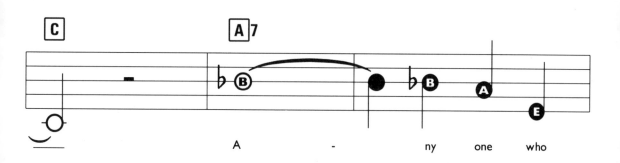

A - ny one who

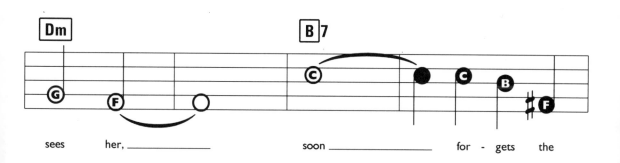

sees her, _____ soon _____ for - gets the

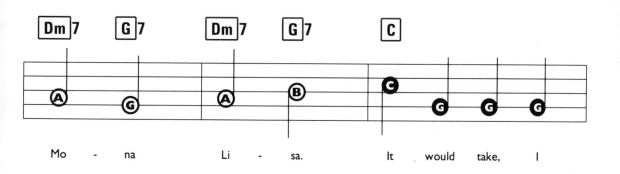

Mo - na Li - sa. It would take, I

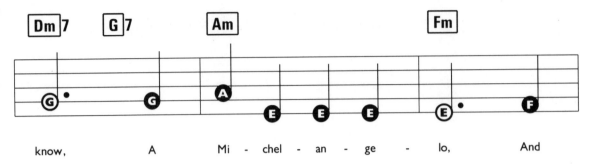

know, A Mi - chel - an - ge - lo, And

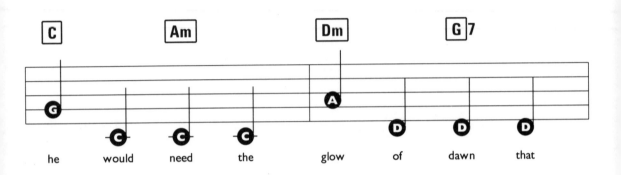

he would need the glow of dawn that

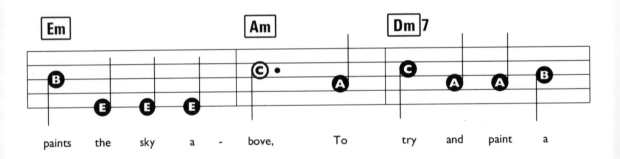

paints the sky a - bove, To try and paint a

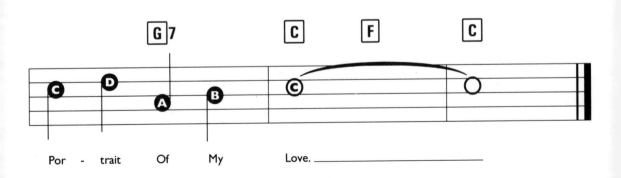

Por - trait Of My Love. _____

Somewhere In The Night

Suggested Registration: FLUTE OR PIANO
Rhythm: ROCK (8 BEAT) OR BALLAD
Tempo: MEDIUM SLOW

Words by Will Jennings
Music by Richard Kerr

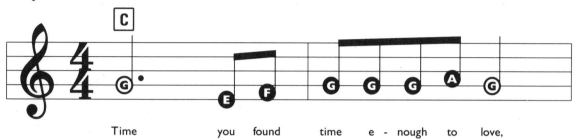

Time you found time e - nough to love,

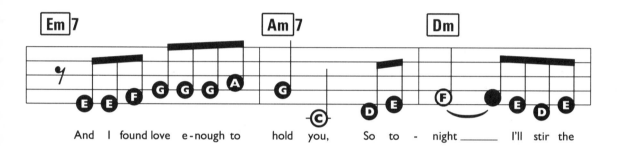

And I found love e-nough to hold you, So to - night _____ I'll stir the

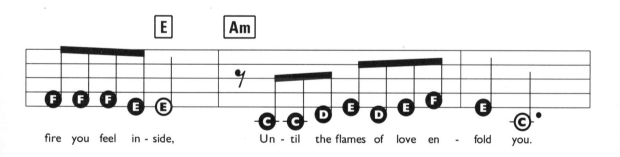

fire you feel in - side, Un - til the flames of love en - fold you.

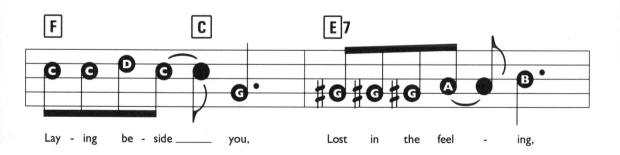

Lay - ing be - side _____ you, Lost in the feel - ing,

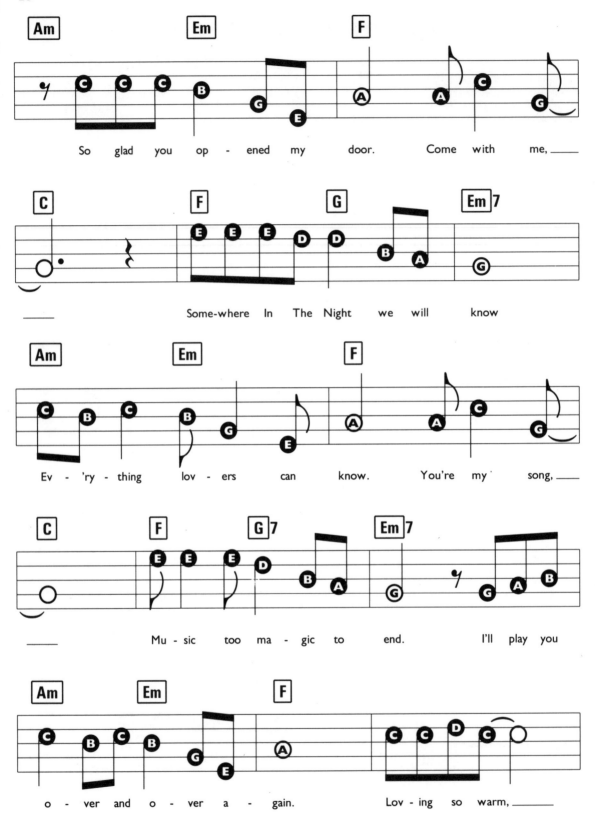

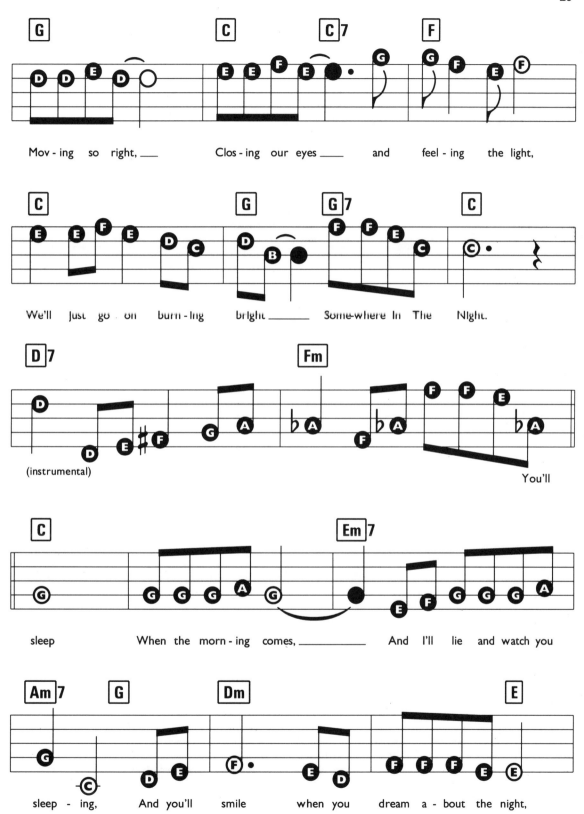

30

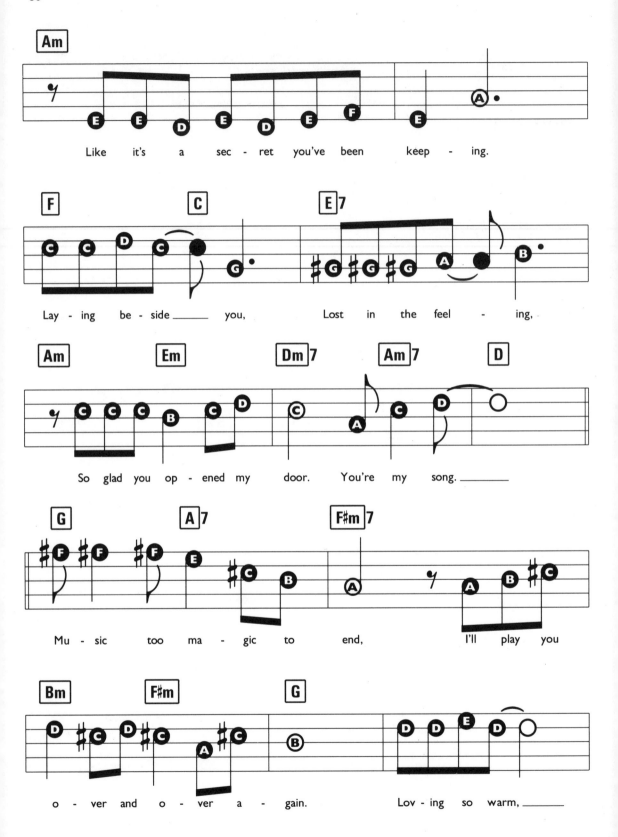

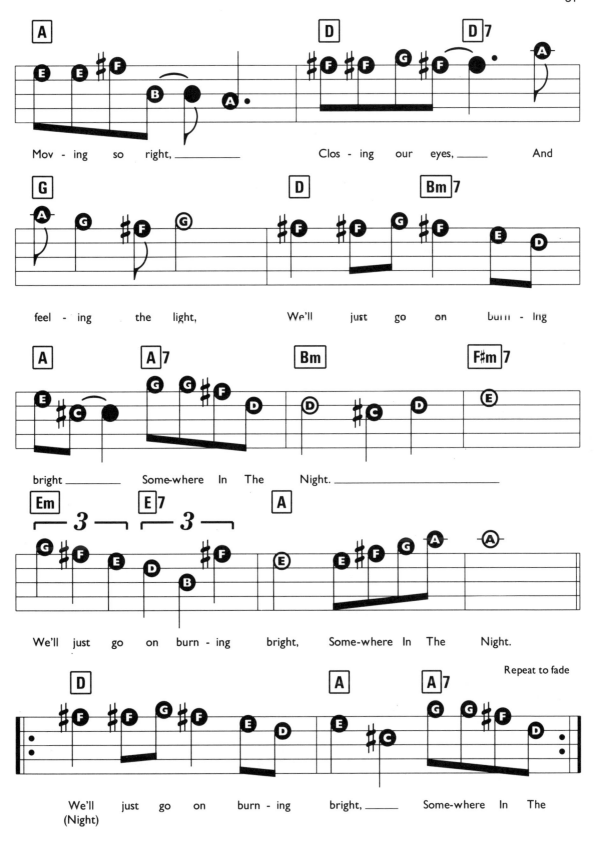

She Makes My Day

Suggested Registration: PIANO OR ACOUSTIC GUITAR
Rhythm: BALLAD
Tempo: SLOW

Words & Music by
Robert Palmer

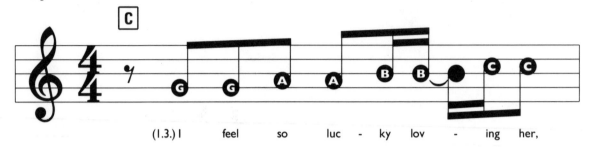

(1.3.) I feel so luc - ky lov - ing her,

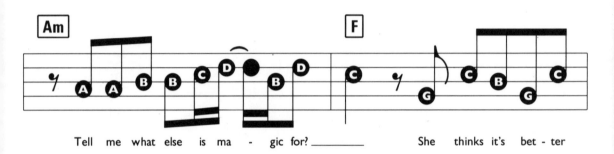

Tell me what else is ma - gic for? _____ She thinks it's bet - ter

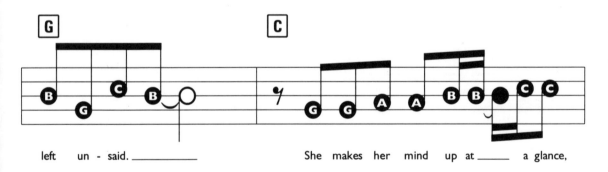

left un - said. _____ She makes her mind up at _____ a glance,

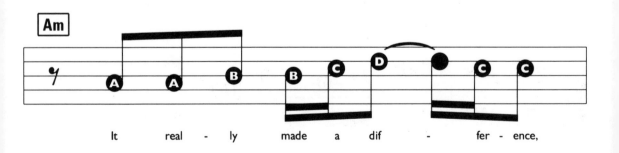

It real - ly made a dif - fer - ence,

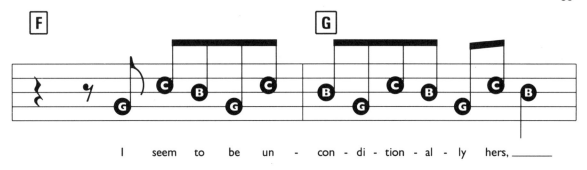

I seem to be un - con - di - tion - al - ly hers, _____

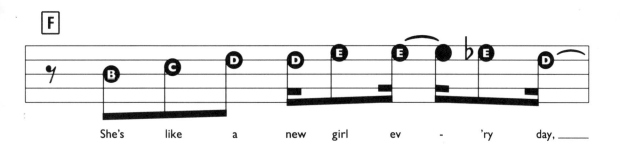

She's like a new girl ev - 'ry day, _____

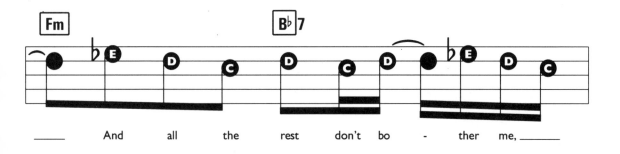

_____ And all the rest don't bo - ther me, _____

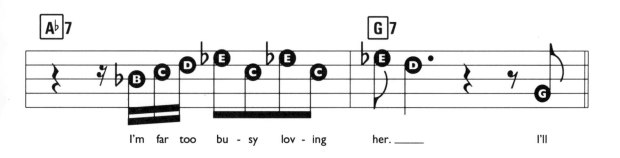

I'm far too bu - sy lov - ing her. _____ I'll

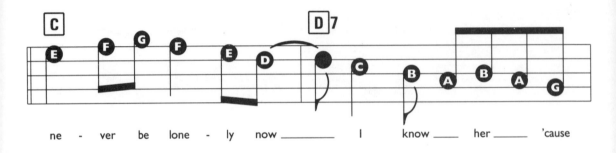

ne - ver be lone - ly now _____ I know ____ her ____ 'cause

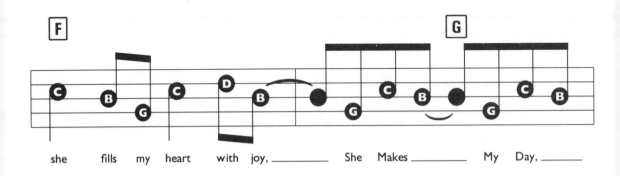

she fills my heart with joy, _____ She Makes _____ My Day, _____

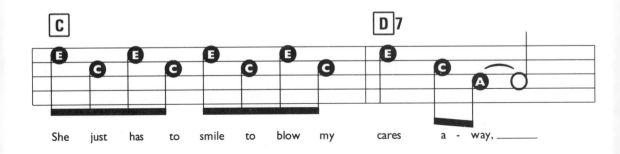

She just has to smile to blow my cares a - way, _____

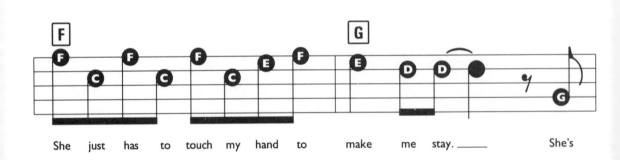

She just has to touch my hand to make me stay. _____ She's

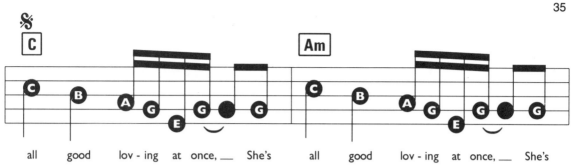

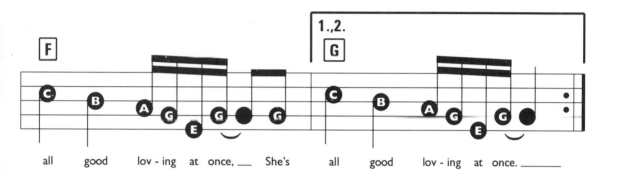

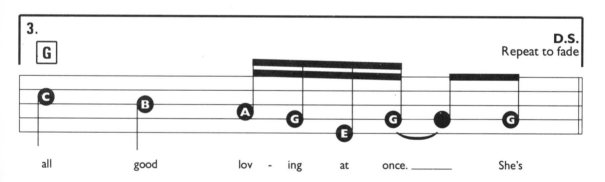

Verse 2:
Our love was unintentional,
She says we're not responsible,
She thinks with her chin up.
She always makes uncommon sense,
She always knows what to say,
She always takes me unawares.
In less time than it takes to fall.
I'm here and there you are,
We never fought it anyway.

To All The Girls I've Loved Before

Suggested Registration: SAXOPHONE OR FLUTE
Rhythm: BALLAD
Tempo: MEDIUM SLOW

Words & Music by
Hal David & Albert Hammond

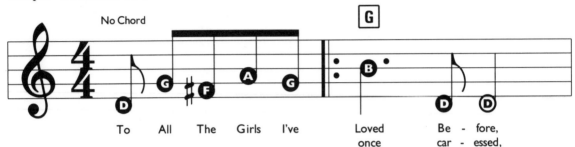

To All The Girls I've Loved Be - fore,
once car - essed,

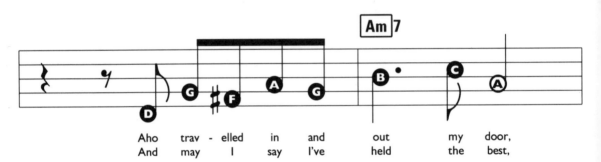

Aho trav - elled in and out my door,
And may I say I've held the best,

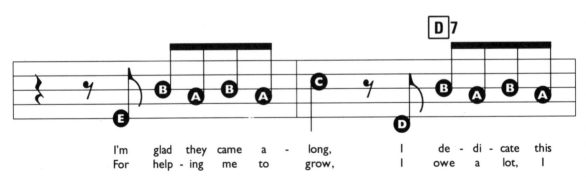

I'm glad they came a - long, I de - di - cate this
For help - ing me to grow, I owe a lot, I

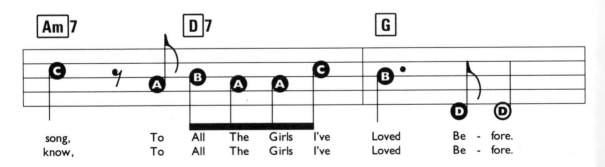

song, To All The Girls I've Loved Be - fore.
know, To All The Girls I've Loved Be - fore.

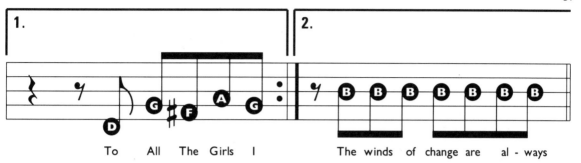

To All The Girls I

The winds of change are al - ways

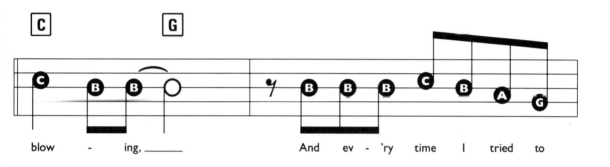

blow - ing, _____

And ev - 'ry time I tried to

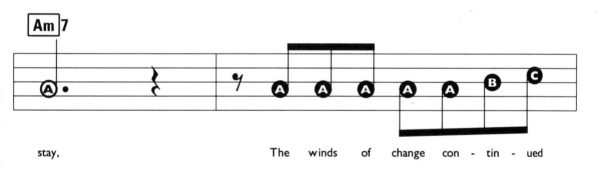

stay,

The winds of change con - tin - ued

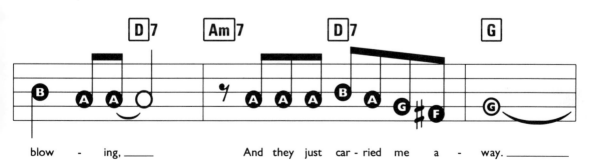

blow - ing, _____

And they just car - ried me a - way. _____

38

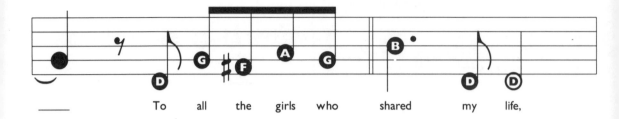

To all the girls who shared my life,

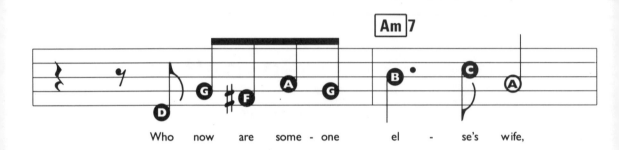

Who now are some - one el - se's wife,

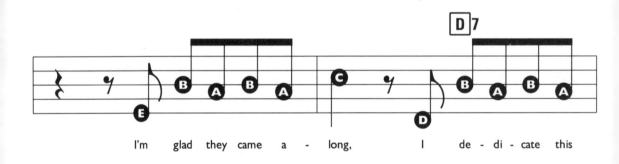

I'm glad they came a - long, I de - di - cate this

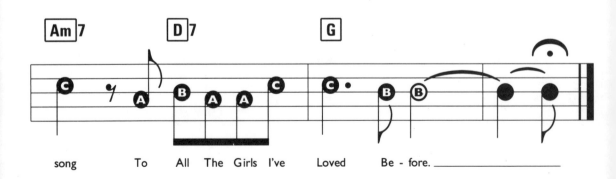

song To All The Girls I've Loved Be - fore. _____

You Are So Beautiful

Suggested Registration: FLUTE OF ACOUSTIC GUITAR
Rhythm: ROCK (8 BEAT) OR BALLAD
Tempo: MEDIUM SLOW

Words & Music by
Billy Preston & Bruce Fisher

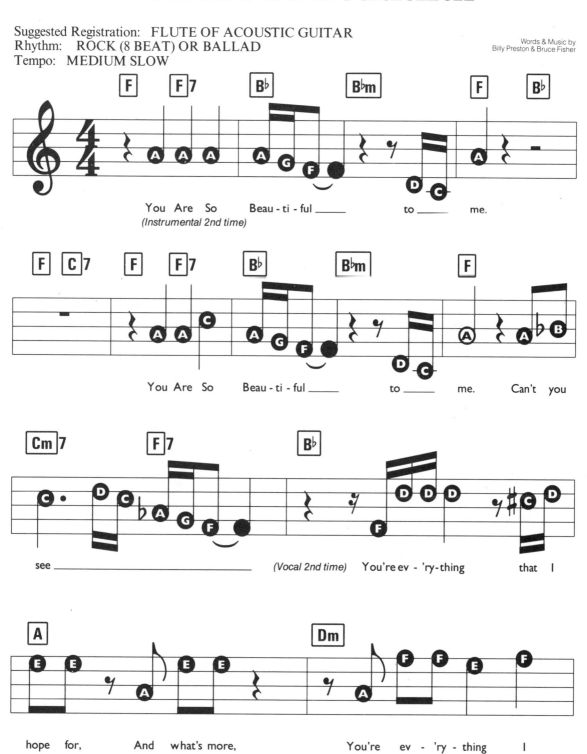

40

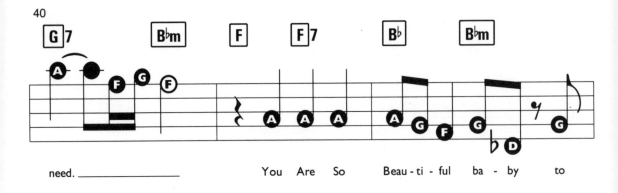

need. _____ You Are So Beau - ti - ful ba - by to

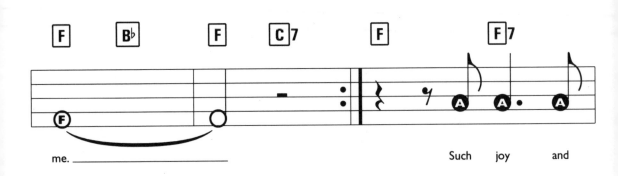

me. _____ Such joy and

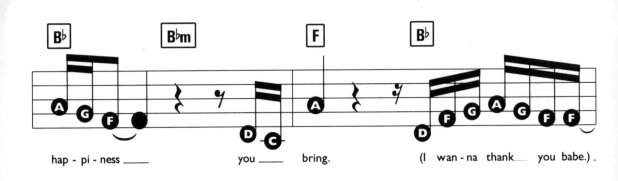

hap - pi - ness ____ you ___ bring. (I wan - na thank ___ you babe.) __

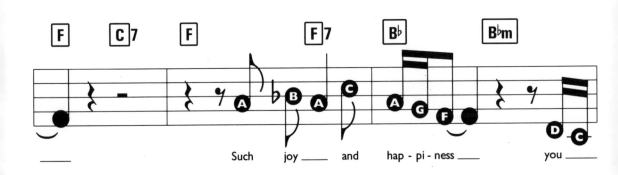

____ Such joy ___ and hap - pi - ness ____ you __

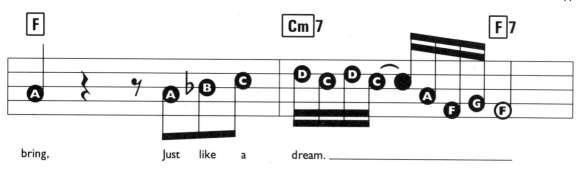

bring,   Just   like   a   dream. _____

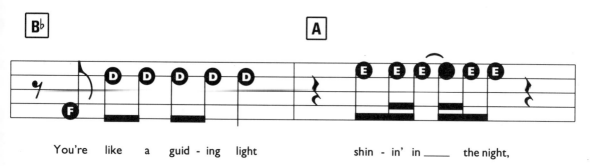

You're   like   a   guid - ing   light   shin - in' in ____ the night,

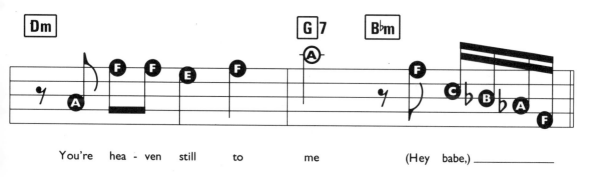

You're   hea - ven   still   to   me   (Hey   babe,) _____

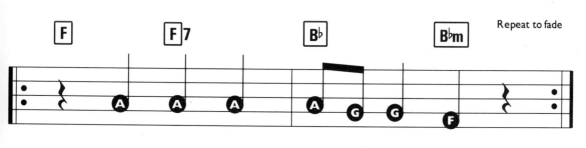

You   Are   So   Beau - ti - ful. _____

Yesterday When I Was Young

Suggested Registration: **VIBRAPHONE OR ELEC. PIANO**
Rhythm: **BALLAD**
Tempo: **MEDIUM**

English Words by Charles Aznavour
Music by Charles Aznavour

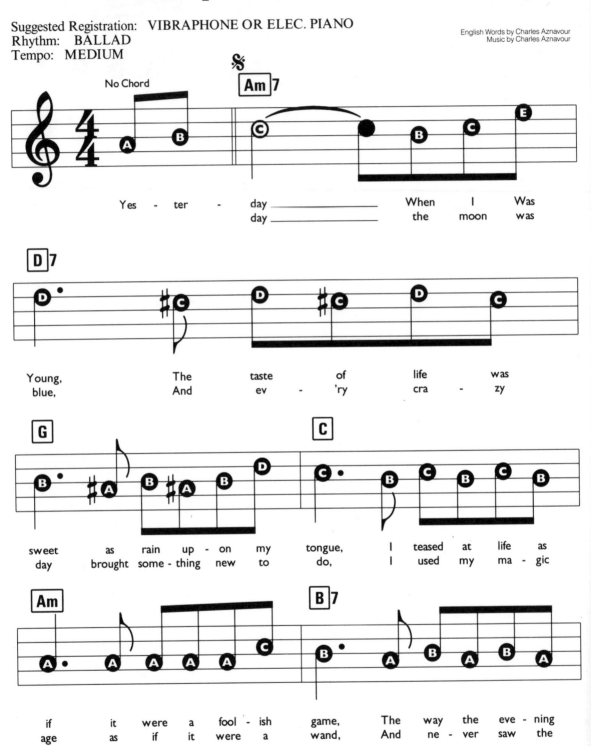

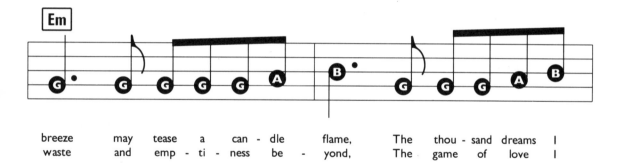

breeze may tease a can - dle flame, The thou - sand dreams I
waste and emp - ti - ness be - yond, The game of love I

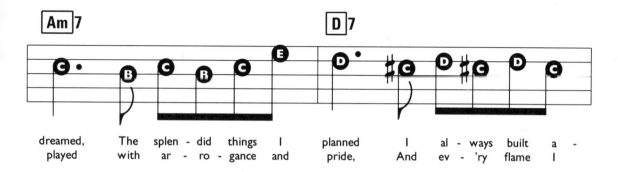

dreamed, The splen - did things I planned I al - ways built a -
played with ar - ro - gance and pride, And ev - 'ry flame I

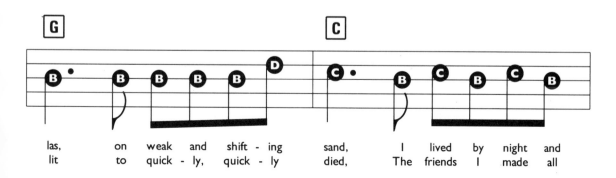

las, on weak and shift - ing sand, I lived by night and
lit to quick - ly, quick - ly died, The friends I made all

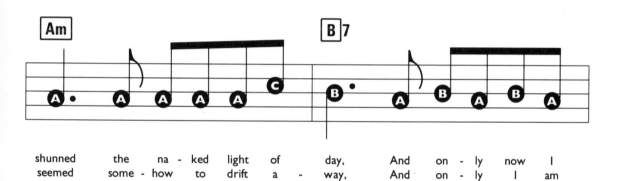

shunned the na - ked light of day, And on - ly now I
seemed some - how to drift a - way, And on - ly I am

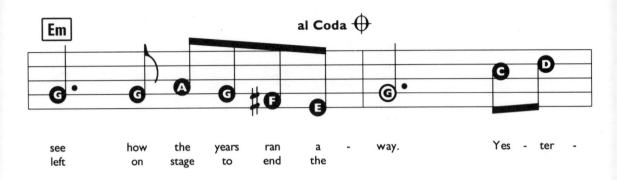

see how the years ran a - way. Yes - ter -
left on stage to end the

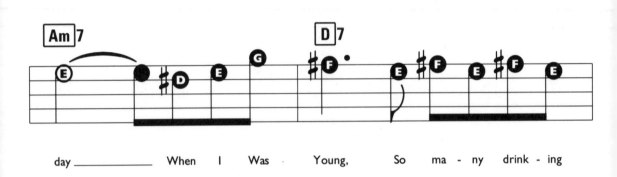

day _____ When I Was Young, So ma - ny drink - ing

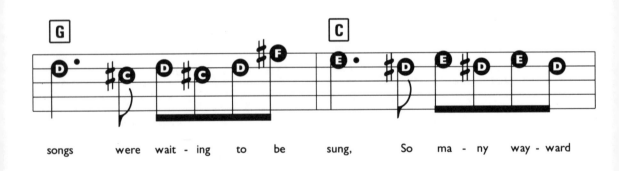

songs were wait - ing to be sung, So ma - ny way - ward

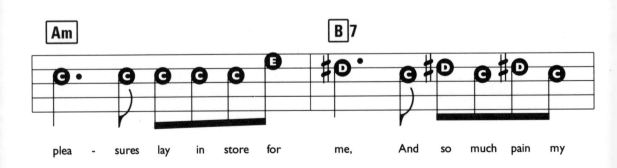

plea - sures lay in store for me, And so much pain my

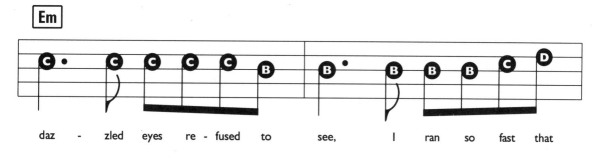

daz - zled eyes re - fused to see, I ran so fast that

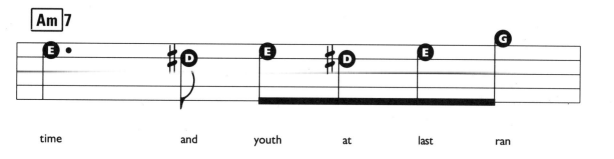

time and youth at last ran

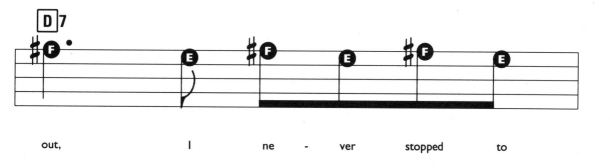

out, I ne - ver stopped to

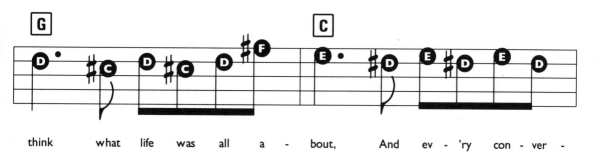

think what life was all a - bout, And ev - 'ry con - ver -

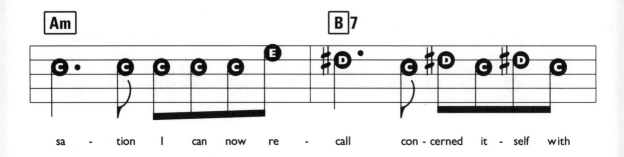

sa - tion   I   can   now   re - call   con - cerned   it - self   with

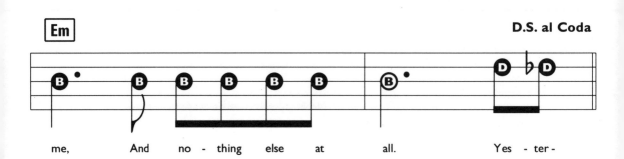

me,   And   no - thing   else   at   all.   Yes - ter-

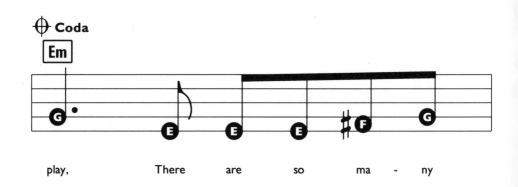

play,   There   are   so   ma - ny

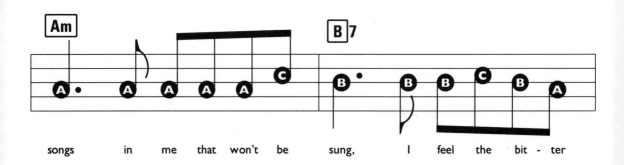

songs   in   me   that   won't   be   sung,   I   feel   the   bit - ter

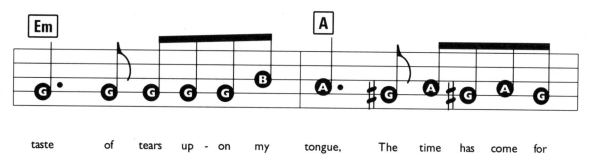

taste   of   tears   up - on   my   tongue,   The   time   has   come   for

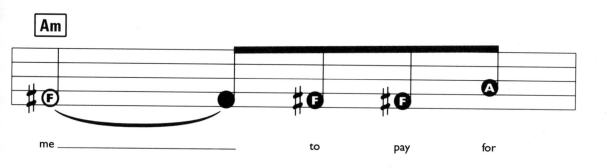

me _____   to   pay   for

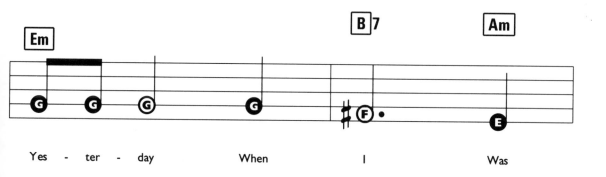

Yes - ter - day   When   I   Was

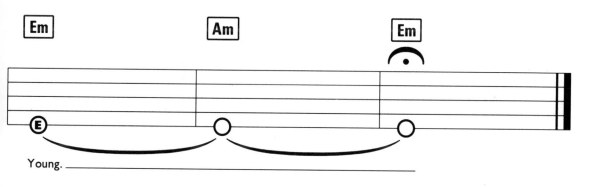

Young. _____

MASTER CHORD CHART

	MAJOR	MINOR	SEVENTH	MINOR SEVENTH
C	5 2 1	5 2 1	5 3 2 1	5 3 2 1
C#/D♭	4 2 1	4 2 1	4 3 2 1	4 3 2 1
D	5 3 1	5 2 1	5 3 2 1	5 3 2 1
E♭	5 3 1	5 3 1	5 3 2 1	5 3 2 1
E	4 3 1	5 3 1	4 3 2 1	5 3 2 1
F	5 3 1	5 3 1	5 3 2 1	5 3 2 1
F#/G♭	4 2 1	4 2 1	5 3 2 1	5 3 2 1
G	5 3 1	5 3 1	5 3 2 1	5 3 2 1
A♭	4 2 1	4 2 1	5 4 2 1	5 4 2 1
A	4 2 1	4 2 1	5 4 2 1	5 4 2 1
B♭	4 2 1	4 2 1	5 4 2 1	5 4 2 1
B	4 2 1	4 2 1	4 3 2 1	4 3 2 1